SCAN THE CODE TO ACCESS YOUR FREE DIGITAL COPY OF THE NEUROANATOMY COLORING BOOK

The Neuroanatomy Coloring Book features:

•The most effective way to skyrocket your neuroanatomical knowledge, all while having fun!

• Full coverage of the major systems of the human brain to provide context and reinforce visual recognition

• 25+ unique, easy-to-color pages of different neuroanatomical sections with their terminology

• Large 8.5 by 11-inch single side paper so you can easily remove your coloring

•Self-quizzing for each page, with convenient same-page answer keys

THIS BOOK BELONGS TO

____

TABLE OF CONTENTS

SCULL (FRONT VIEW)

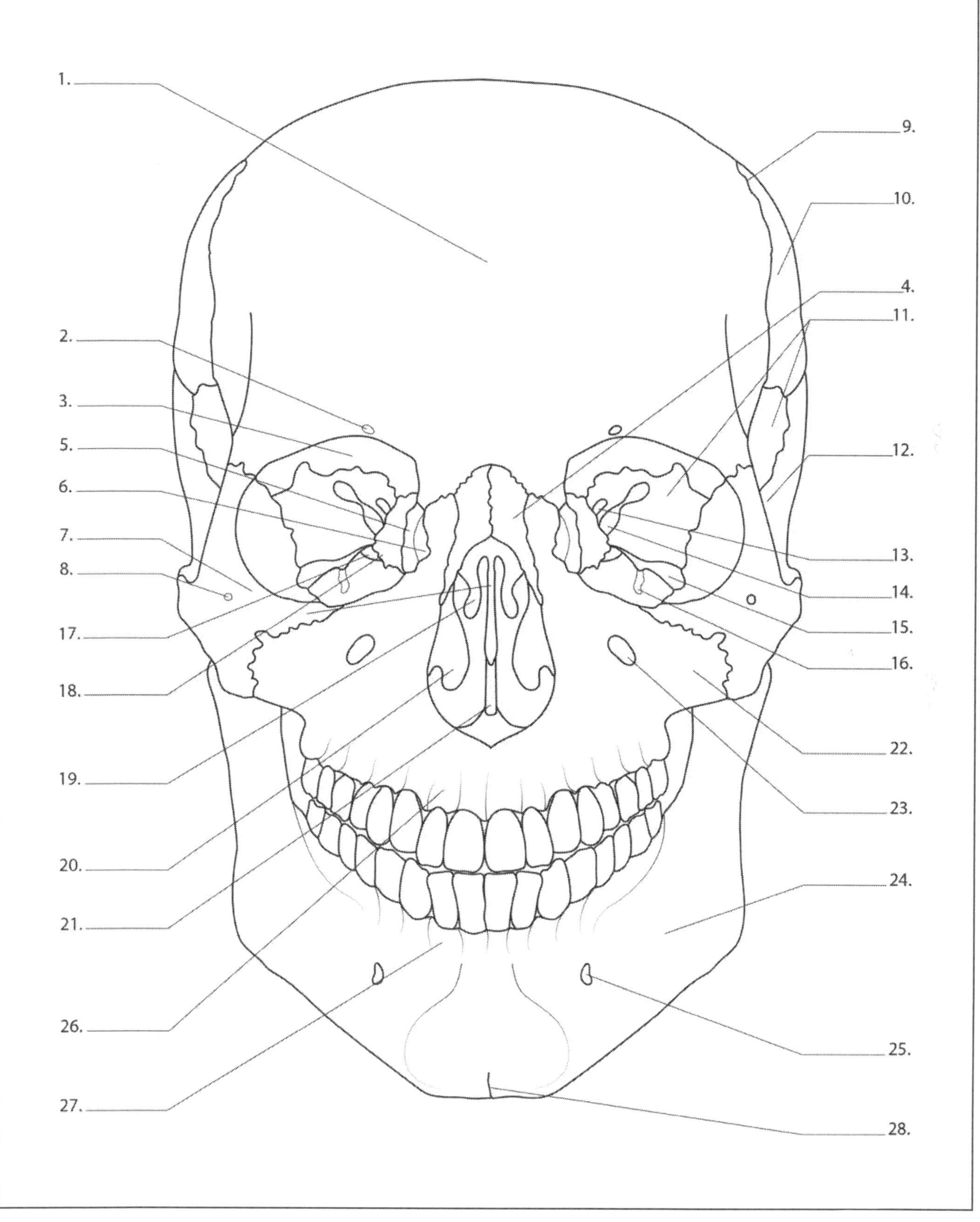

SCULL (FRONT VIEW)

1. Frontal bone
2. Supraorbital foramen
3. Orbit
4. Nasal bone
5. Lacrimal bone
6. Lacrimal fossa
7. Zygomatic bone
8. Zygomaticofacial fossa
9. Coronal suture
10. Parietal bone
11. Sphenoid bone
12. Temporal bone
13. Optic canal
14. Superior orbital fissure
15. Inferior orbital fissure
16. Infraorbital sulcus
17. Palatine bone
18. Ethmoid bone
19. Middle concha
20. Inferior concha
21. Vomer
22. Maxilla
23. Infraorbital foramen
24. Mandible
25. Mental foramen
26. Alveolar process of maxilla
27. Alveolar process of mandible
28. Mental protuberance of mandible

CRANIAL BASE (EXTERNAL VIEW)

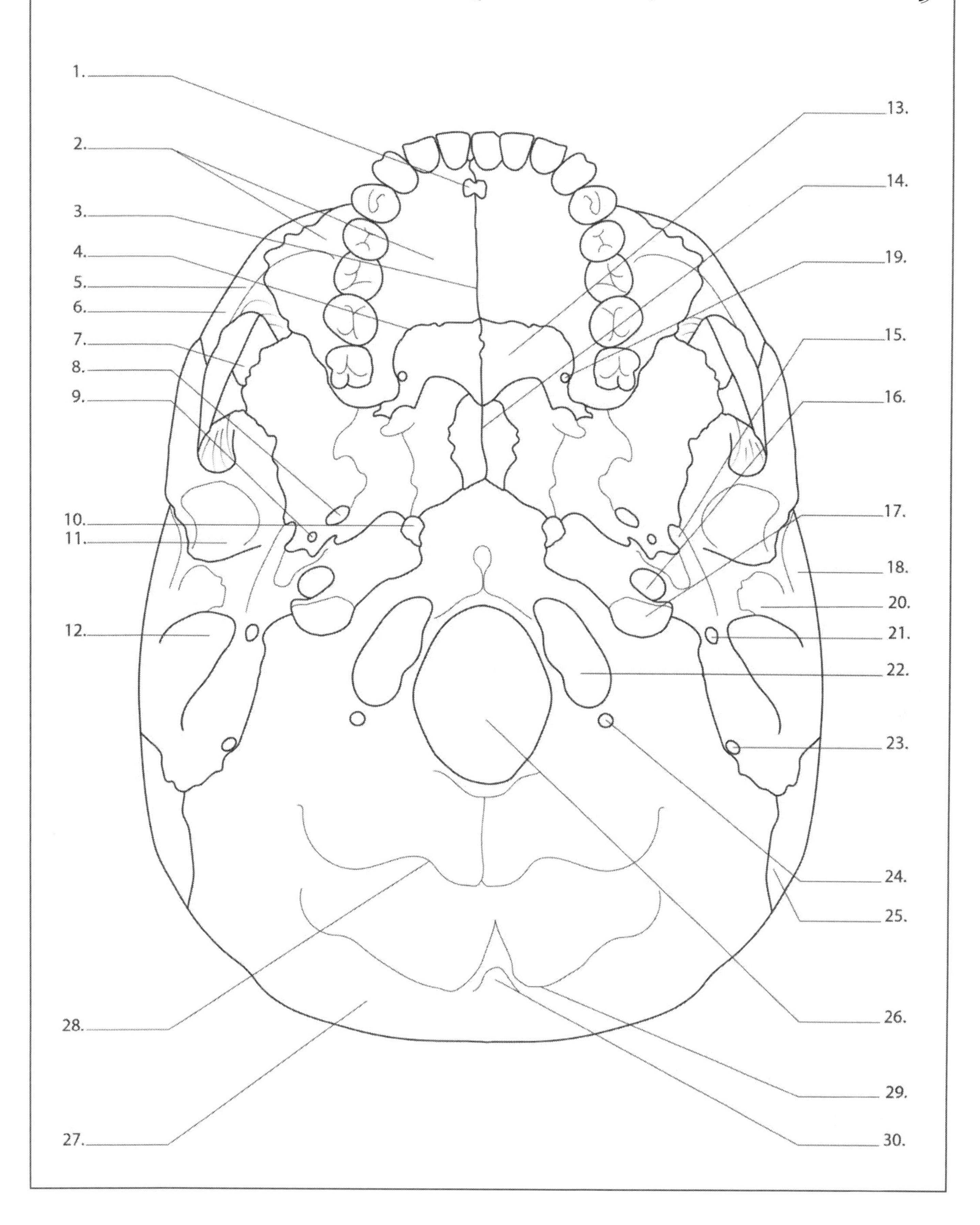

CRANIAL BASE (EXTERNAL VIEW)

1. Incisive foramen
2. Maxilla
3. Median palatine suture
4. Transverse palatine suture
5. Zygomatic bone
6. Zygomatic arch
7. Frontal bone
8. Foramen ovale (oval window)
9. Foramen spinosum
10. Foramen lacerum (lacerated piercing)
11. Mandibular fossa
12. Mastoid process
13. Palatine bone
14. Vomer
15. Styloid process
16. Carotid canal
17. Jugular foramen
18. Temporal bone
19. Greater palatine foramina
20. External acoustic meatus
21. Stylomastoid foramen
22. Occipital condyle
23. Mastoid foramen
24. Condylar fossa
25. Parietal bone
26. Foramen magnum
27. Occipital bone
28. Inferior nuchal line
29. Superior nuchal line
30. External occipital protuberance

CRANIAL BASE (INTERNAL VIEW)

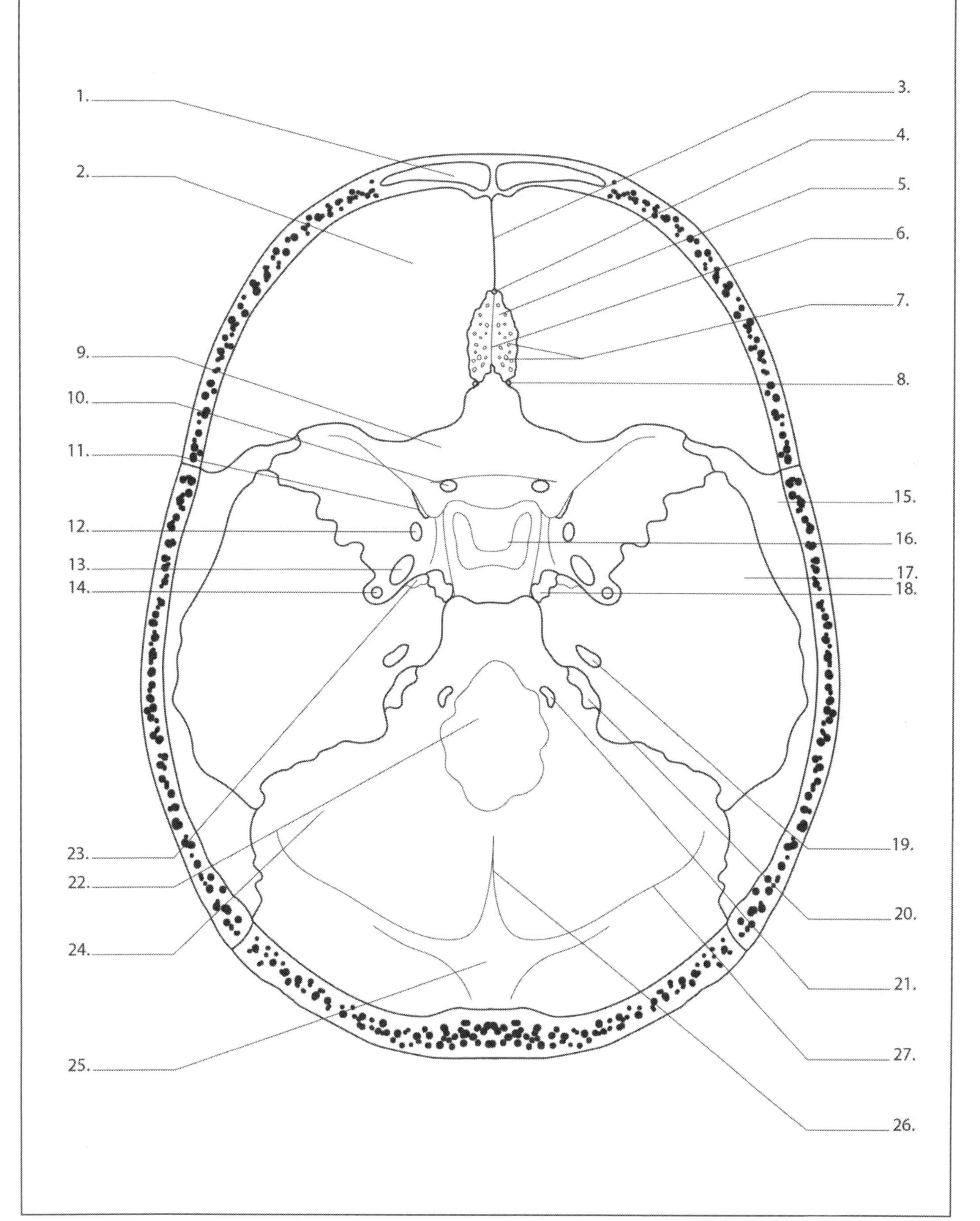

CRANIAL BASE (INTERNAL VIEW)

1. Frontal sinus
2. Frontal bone
3. Frontal crest
4. Foramen caecum
5. Ethmoid bone
6. Crista galli
7. Cribriform plate
8. Foramen ethmoid posterior
9. Sphenoid bone
10. Optic foramen
11. Fissure orbitalis superior
12. Foramen rotundum
13. Foramen ovale (oval window)
14. Foramen spinosum
15. Parietal bone
16. Sella turcica
17. Temporal bone
18. Foramen lacerum (lacerated piercing)
19. Internal auditory canal
20. Jugular foramen
21. Hypoglossal canal
22. Foramen magnum
23. Carotid canal
24. Occipital bone
25. Internal occipital protuberance
26. Internal occipital crest
27. Groove for the transverse sinus

TEMPOROMANDIBULAR JOINT (LATERAL VIEW)

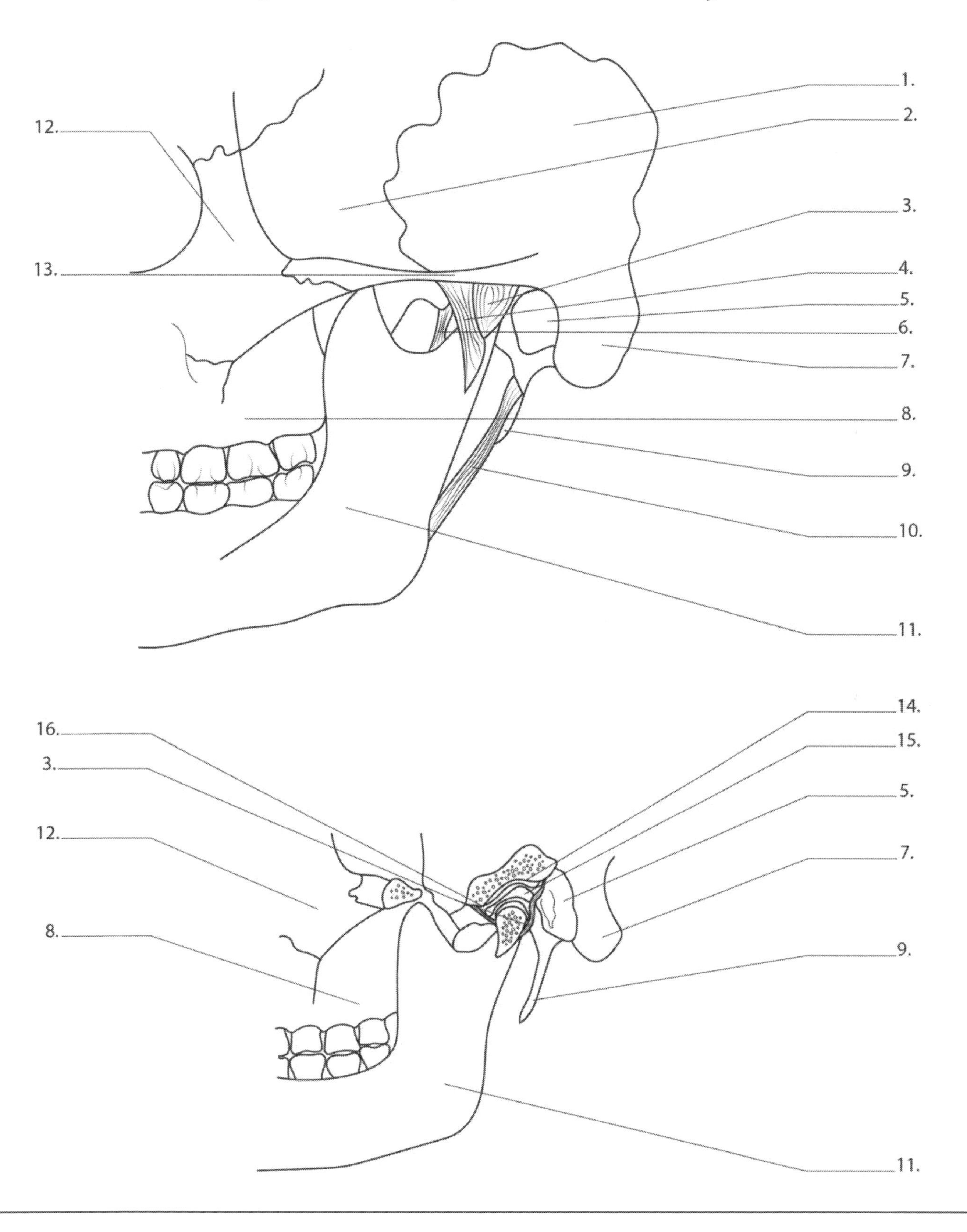

TEMPOROMANDIBULAR JOINT (LATERAL VIEW)

1. Temporal bone
2. Sphenoid bone
3. Articular capsule
4. Lateral ligament
5. External acoustic meatus
6. Sphenomandibular ligament (internal lateral ligament)
7. Mastoid process
8. Maxilla
9. Styloid process
10. Stylomandibular ligament
11. Ramus of mandible
12. Zygomatic bone
13. Zygomatic arch
14. Fossa mandible
15. Articular disc
16. Articular tubercle

MUSCLES OF FACE (FRONT VIEW)

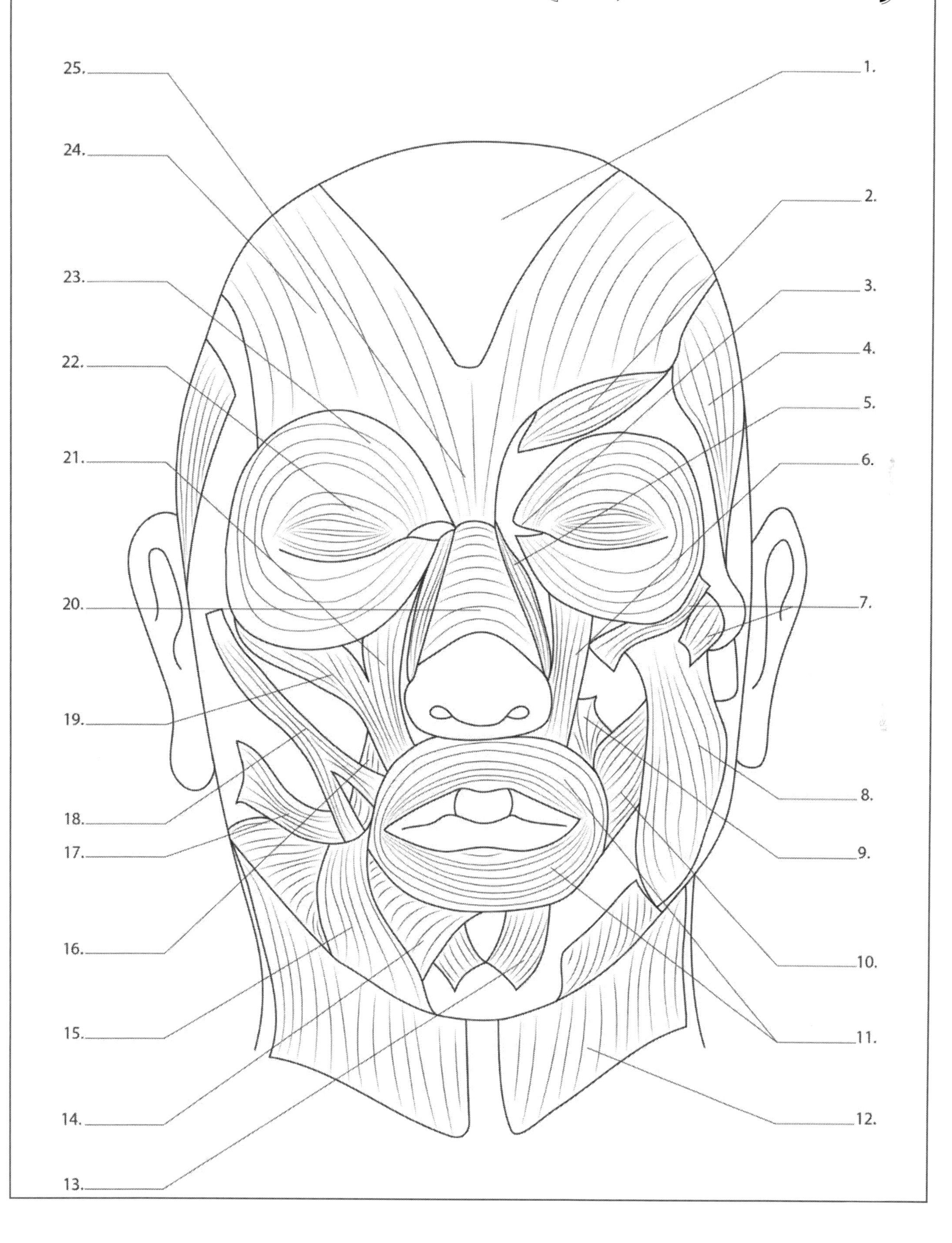

MUSCLES OF FACE (FRONT VIEW)

1. Epicranial aponeurosis
2. Muscle corrugator supercilii
3. Muscle levator labii superioris alaeque nasi
4. Muscle temporalis
5. Muscle nasalis (transverse nasalis)
6. Muscle levator labii superior
7. Muscle zygomaticus minor and major
8. Muscle masseter
9. Muscle levator anguli oris
10. Muscle buccinator
11. Muscle orbicularis oris
12. Platysma
13. Muscle mentalis
14. Muscle depressor labii inferioris
15. Muscle depressor anguli oris
16. Muscle levator anguli oris
17. Muscle risorius
18. Muscle zygomaticus major
19. Muscle zygomaticus minor
20. Muscle nasalis (alar nasalis)
21. Muscle levator labii superioris
22. Muscle orbicularis oculi (palpebral portion)
23. Muscle orbicularis oculi (orbitalis portion)
24. Muscle occipitofrontalis (frontal portion)
25. Muscle procerus

MUSCLES OF FACE AND NECK (LATERAL VIEW)

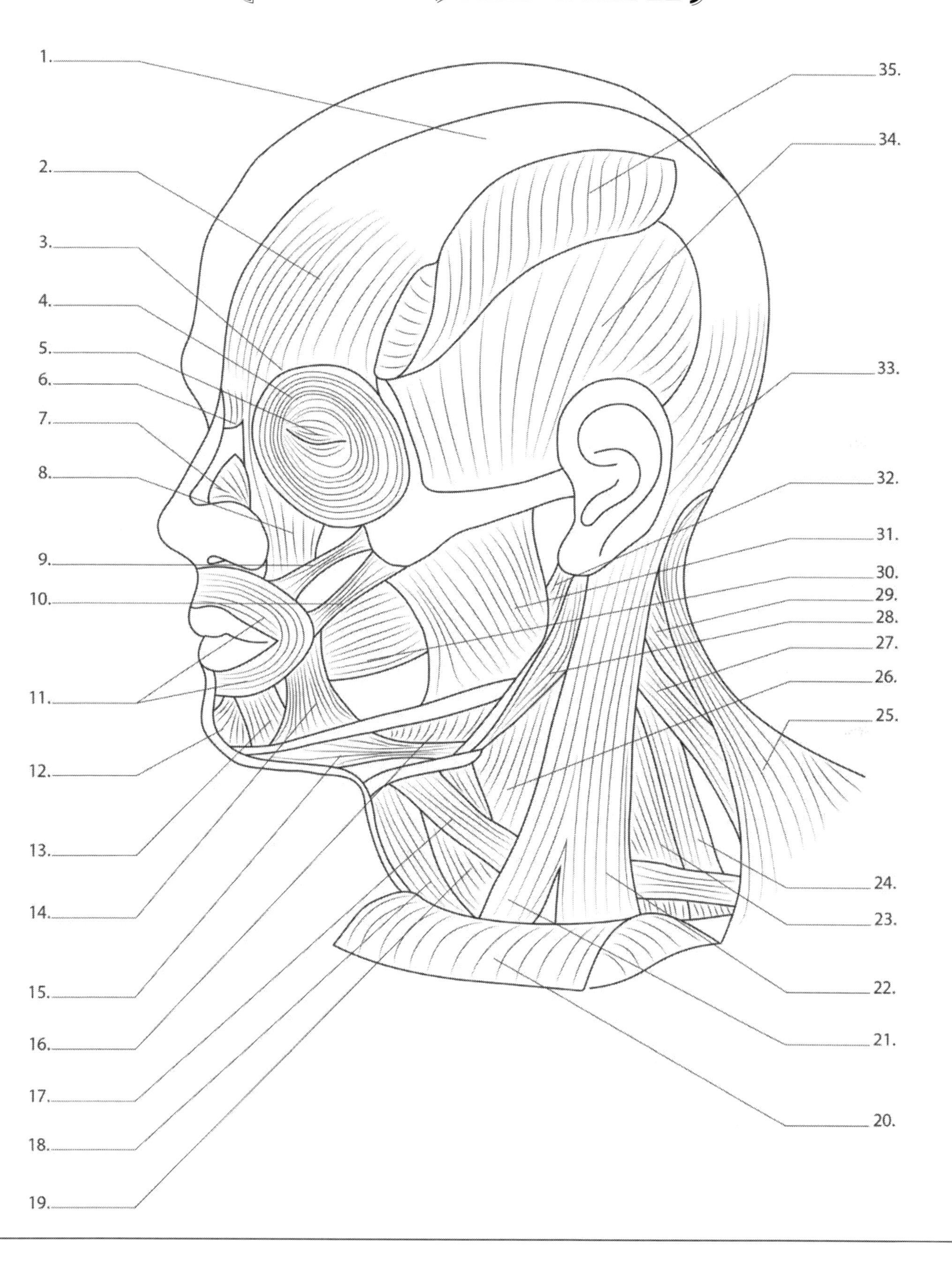

MUSCLES OF FACE AND NECK (LATERAL VIEW)

1. Epicranial aponeurosis
2. Frontal belly of occipitofrontalis muscle
3. Muscle corrugator suprcilii
4. Muscle orbicularis oculi (palpebral portion)
5. Muscle orbicularis oculi (orbitalis portion)
6. Muscle procerus
7. Muscle nasalis
8. Muscle levator labii superiorus
9. Muscle zygomaticus minor
10. Muscle zygomaticus major
11. Muscle orbicularis oris
12. Muscle mentalis
13. Muscle depressor labii inferioris
14. Muscle depressor anguli oris
15. Muscle digastric (anterior belly)
16. Muscle mylohyoid
17. Muscle omohyoid
18. Muscle sternohyoid
19. Muscle thyrohyoid
20. Platisma
21. Muscle sternocleidomastoid (sternal head)
22. Muscle sternocleidomastoid (clavicular head)
23. Muscle scalene medium
24. Muscle scalene posterior
25. Muscle trapezius
26. Muscle constrictor pharynx
27. Muscle levator scapula
28. Muscle digastric (posterior belly)
29. Muscle splenius
30. Muscle buccinator
31. Muscle masseter
32. Muscle stylohyoid
33. Occipital belly of occipitofrontalis muscle
34. Muscle temporalis
35. Muscle temporoparietalis

BONES OF HEAD AND NECK (LATERAL VIEW)

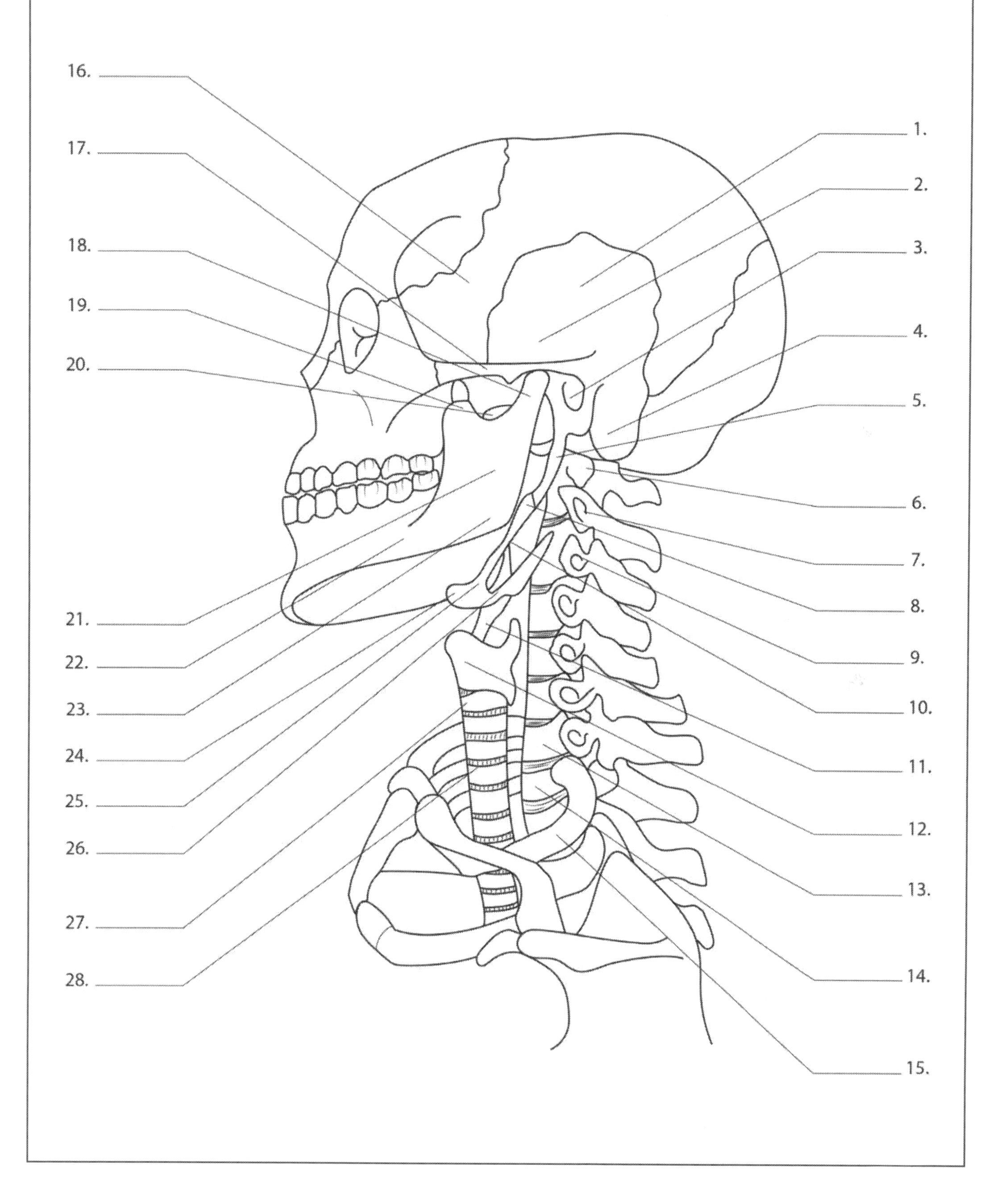

BONES OF HEAD AND NECK (LATERAL VIEW)

1. Temporal bone
2. Temporal fossa
3. External acoustic meatus
4. Mastoid process
5. Styloid process
6. Atlas (C1)
7. Axis (C2)
8. Stylomandibular ligament
9. C3 vertebra
10. Stylohyoid ligament
11. Epiglottis
12. Thyroid cartilage
13. C7 vertebra
14. T1 vertebra
15. 1st rib
16. Sphenoid bone
17. Zygomatic arch
18. Condylar process of mandible
19. Coronoid process of mandible
20. Mandibular notch (incisura)
21. Ramus of mandible
22. Body of mandible
23. Angle of mandible
24. Body of hyoid bone
25. Lesser horn of hyoid bone
26. Greater horn of hyoid bone
27. Cricoid cartilage
28. Trachea

CHEST MUSCLES (FRONT VIEW)

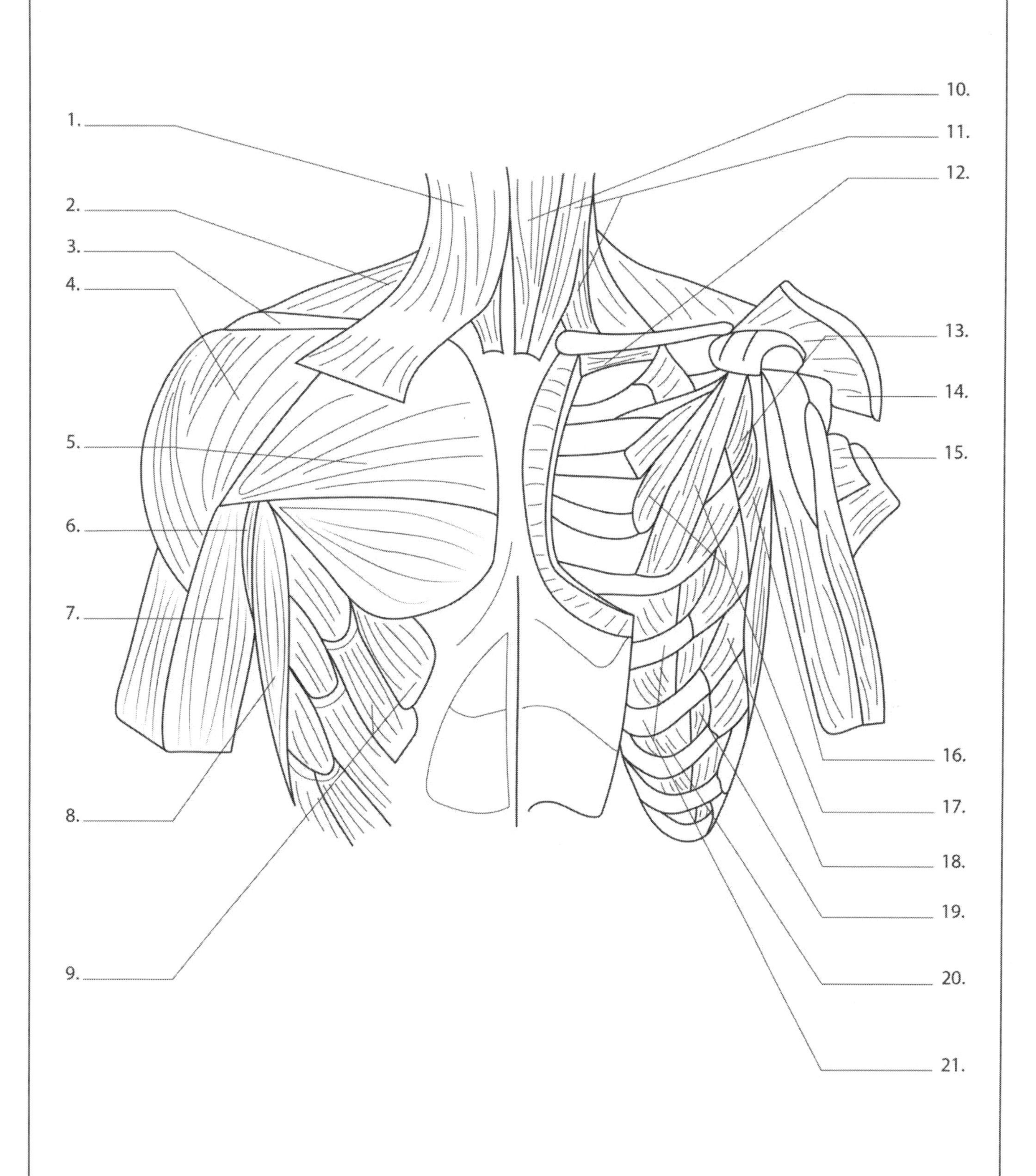

CHEST MUSCLES (FRONT VIEW)

1. Muscle platysma
2. Muscle trapezius
3. Muscle clavicle
4. Muscle deltoid
5. Muscle pectoralis major
6. Muscle coracobrachialis
7. Muscle biceps brachii
8. Muscle latissimus dorsi
9. Muscle external abdominal oblique
10. Muscle sternohyoid
11. Muscle sternocleidomastoid
12. Muscle subclavius
13. Muscle deltoid (cut)
14. Muscle subscapularis
15. Muscle pectoralis major (cut)
16. Muscle teres major
17. Muscle pectoralis minor
18. Muscle serratus anterior
19. Muscle external intercostal
20. Muscle internal intercostal
21. Ribs

CHEST MUSCLES (BACK VIEW)

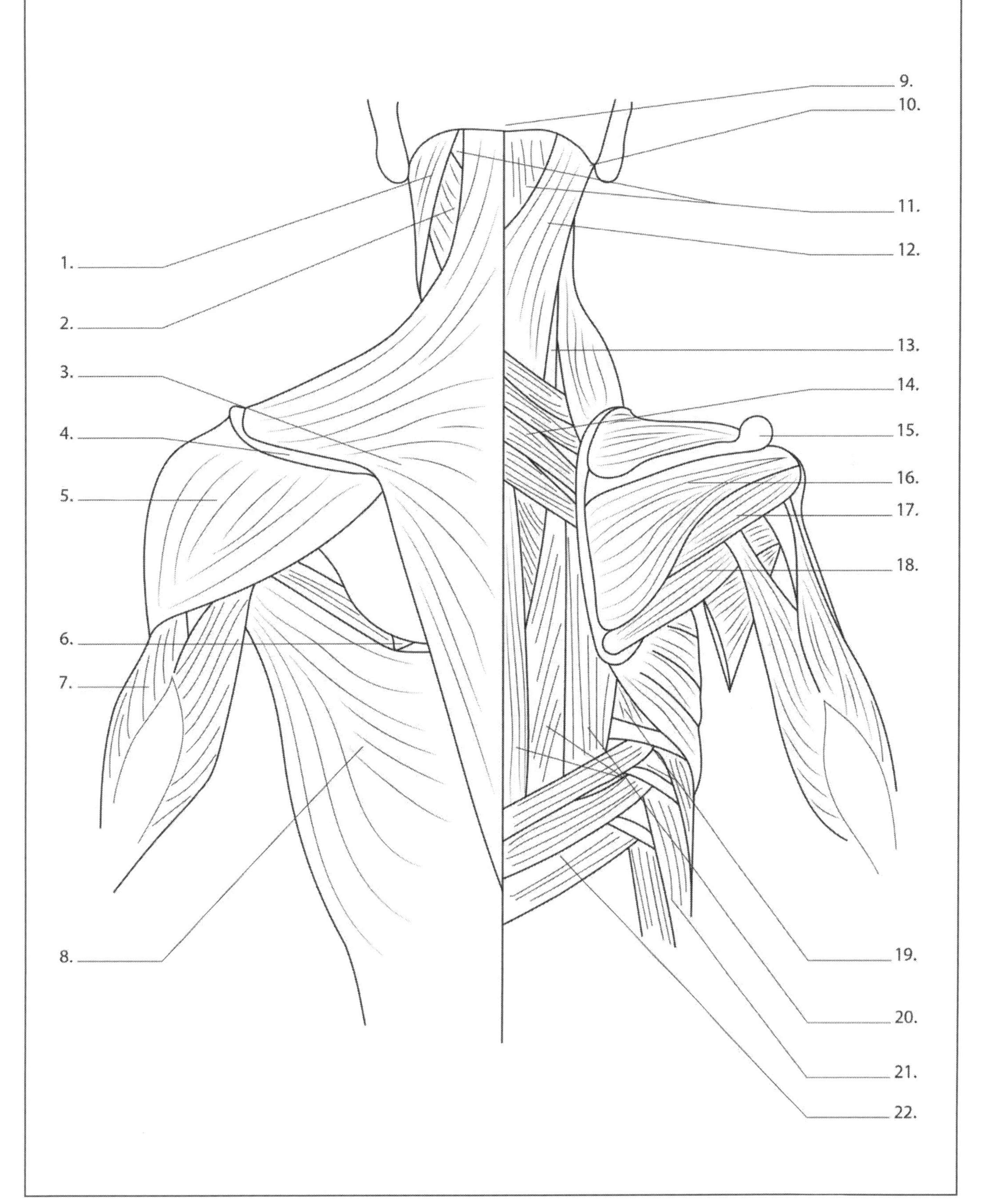

CHEST MUSCLES (BACK VIEW)

1. Muscle sternocleidomastoid
2. Muscle splenius capitis
3. Muscle trapezius
4. Spina scapula
5. Muscle deltoid
6. Inferior angle of scapula
7. Muscle triceps brachii
8. Muscle latissimus dorsi
9. External occipital protuberance
10. Mastoid process of temporal bone
11. Muscle semispinalis capitis
12. Muscle splenius capitis
13. Muscle splenius cervicis
14. Muscle serratus posterior superior
15. Acromion process of scapula
16. Muscle infraspinatus
17. Muscle teres minor
18. Muscle teres major
19. Muscle external intercostals
20. Muscle erector spinae (group)
21. Muscle external abdominal oblique
22. Muscle serratus posterior inferior

CHEST BONES (FRONT AND BACK VIEW)

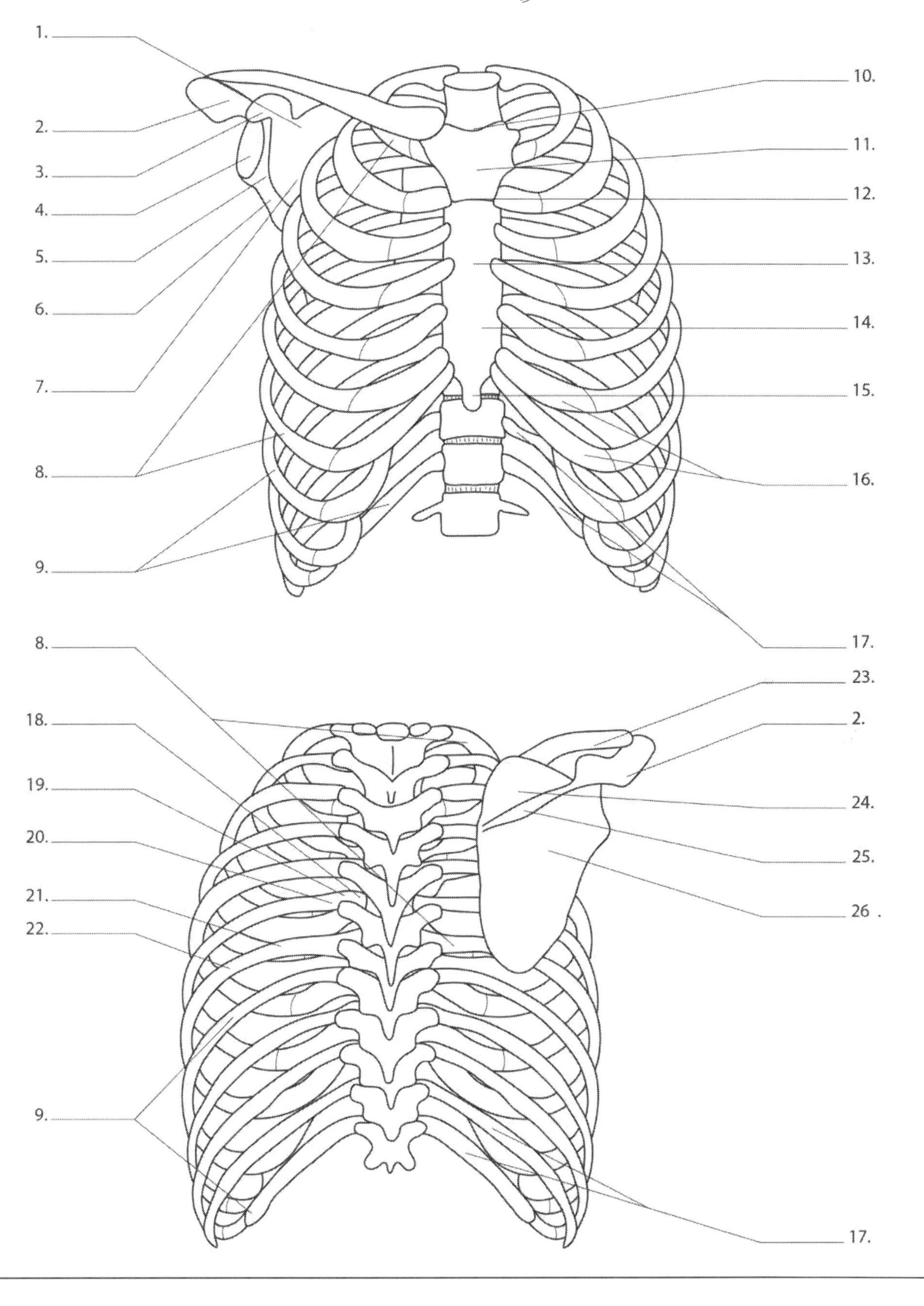

CHEST BONES (FRONT AND BACK VIEW)

1. Suprascapular notch
2. Acromion of scapula
3. Coracoid process of scapula
4. Glenoid cavity of scapula
5. Neck of scapula
6. Scapula
7. Subscapular fossa
8. True ribs (1-7)
9. False ribs (8-12)
10. Jugular notch of sternum
11. Manubrium of sternum
12. Angle of sternum
13. Body of sternum
14. Sternum
15. Xiphoid process
16. Costal cartilages
17. Floating ribs (11-12)
18. Head of ribs
19. Neck of ribs
20. Tubercle of ribs
21. Angle of ribs
22. Body of ribs
23. Clavicle
24. Supraspinous fossa of scapula
25. Spina of scapula
26. Infraspinous fossa of scapula

ORGANS OF THORACIC CAVITY (FRONT VIEW)

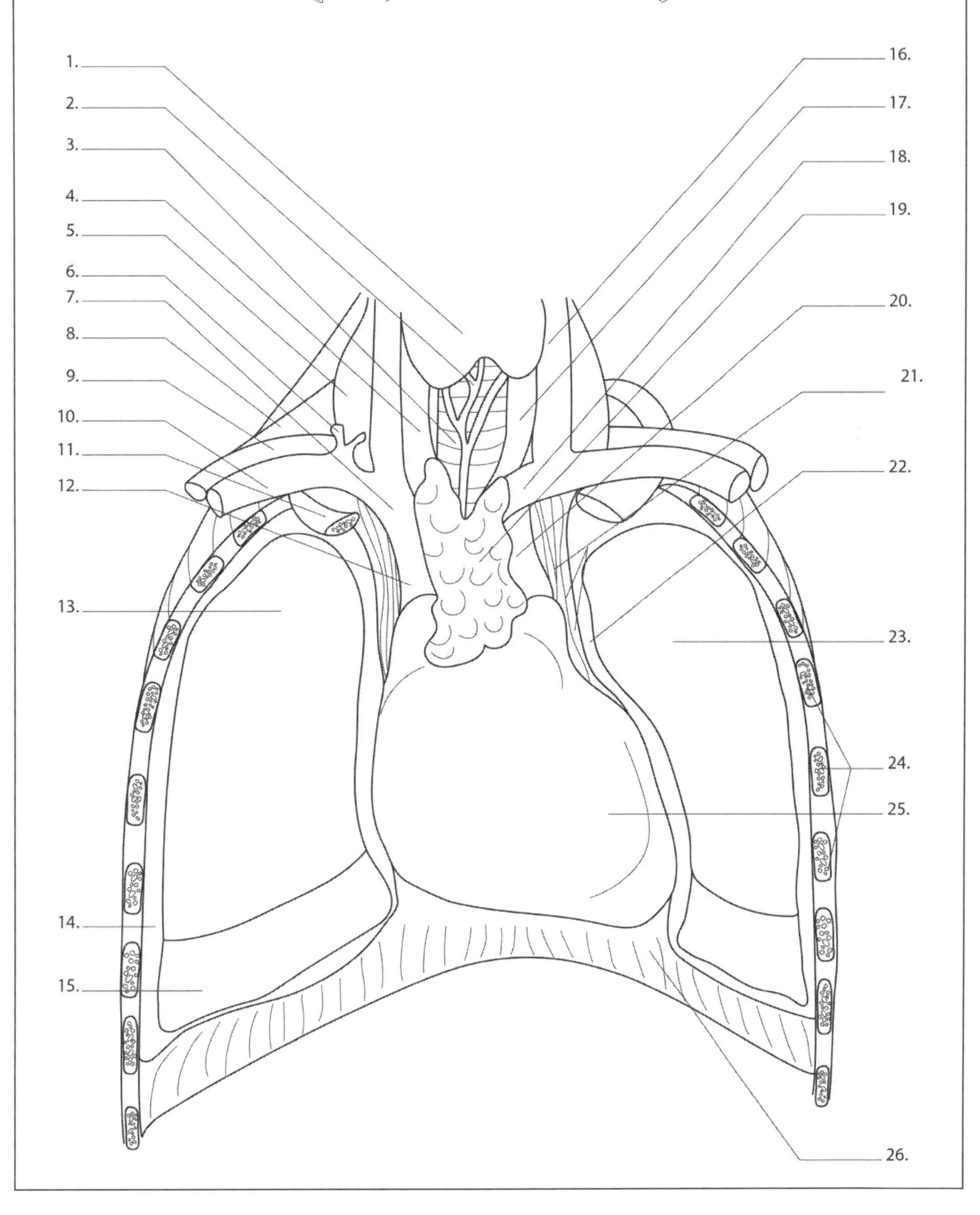

ORGANS OF THORACIC CAVITY (FRONT VIEW)

1. Thyroid gland
2. Inferior thyroid vein
3. Trachea
4. Brachiocephalic trunk
5. Anterior scalene muscle
6. External jugular vein
7. Right brachiocephalic vein
8. Brachial plexus
9. Subclavian artery
10. Subclavian vein
11. 1st rib
12. Superior vena cava
13. Right lung
14. Costal part of parietal pleura
15. Diaphragmatic part of parietal pleura
16. Internal jugular vein
17. Left common carotid artery
18. Left brachiocephalic vein
19. Thymus gland
20. Arch of aorta
21. Phrenic nerve and pericardiacophrenic artery and vein
22. Left lung
23. Ribs
24. Heart
25. Diaphragm

LUNGS

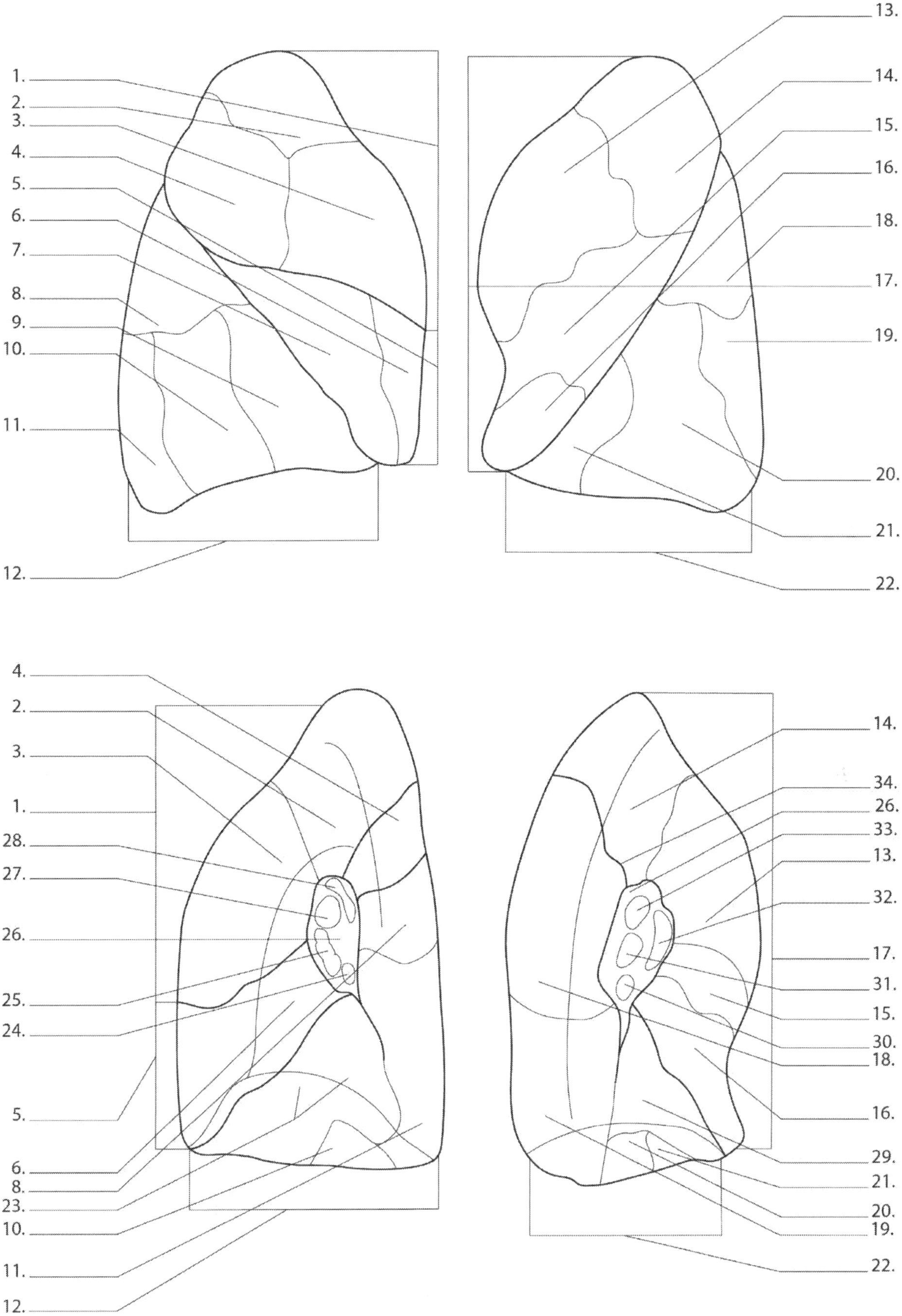

1.
2.
3.
4.
5.
6.
7.
8.
9.
10.
11.
12.

13.
14.
15.
16.
18.
17.
19.
20.
21.
22.

4.
2.
3.
1.
28.
27.
26.
25.
24.
5.
6.
8.
23.
10.
11.
12.

14.
34.
26.
33.
13.
32.
17.
31.
15.
30.
18.
16.
29.
21.
20.
19.
22.

LUNGS

1. Superior lobe of right lung
2. Apical segment of superior lobe of right lung
3. Anterior segment of superior lobe of right lung
4. Posterior segment of superior lobe of right lung
5. Middle lobe of right lung
6. Medial segment of middle lobe of right lung
7. Lateral segment of middle lobe of right lung
8. Superior segment of inferior lobe of right lung
9. Anterior basal segment of inferior lobe of right lung
10. Lateral basal segment of inferior lobe of right lung
11. Posterior basal segment of inferior lobe of right lung
12. Inferior lobe of right lung
13. Anterior segment of superior lobe of left lung
14. Apical-posterior segment of superior lobe of left lung
15. Superior lingular segment of superior lobe of left lung
16. Inferior lingular segment of superior lobe of left lung
17. Superior lobe of left lung
18. Superior segment or inferior lobe of left lung
19. Posterior basal segment or inferior lobe of left lung
20. Lateral basal segment or inferior lobe of left lung
21. Anterior basal segment or inferior lobe of left lung
22. Inferior lobe of left lung
23. Medial basal segment of inferior lobe of right lung
24. Right inferior pulmonary vein
25. Right superior pulmonary vein
26. Hilum
27. Right pulmonary artery
28. Right superior bronchi of right lung
29. Anterior medial basal segment of inferior lobe of left lung
30. Inferior pulmonary vein of left lung
31. Rami bronchi of left lung
32. Left superior pulmonary vein
33. Left pulmonary artery
34. Oblique fissure

HEART (DIAPHRAGMATIC VIEW)

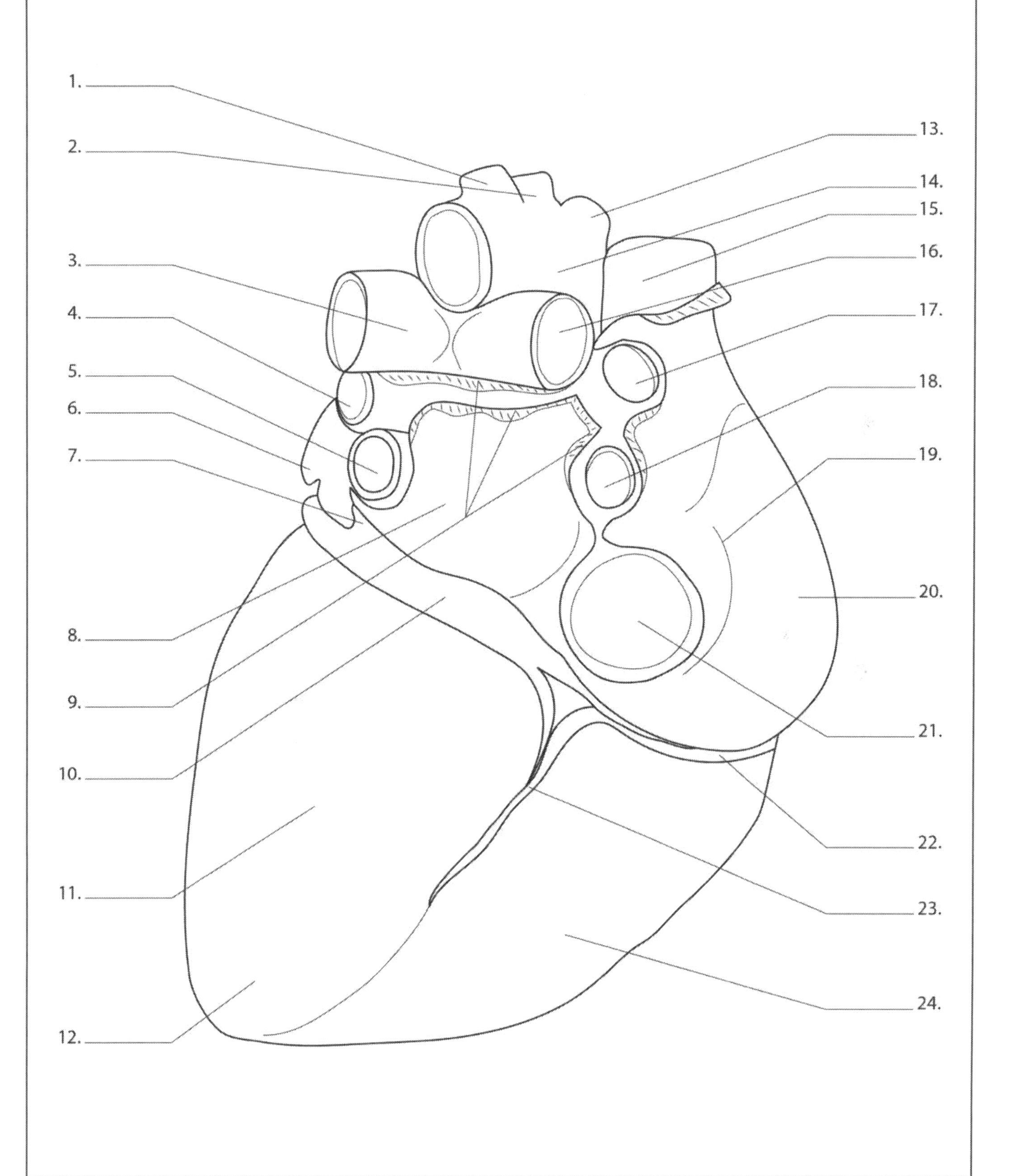

HEART (DIAPHRAGMATIC VIEW)

1. Left subclavian artery
2. Left common carotid artery
3. Left pulmonary artery
4. Left superior pulmonary vein
5. Left inferior pulmonary vein
6. Left auricle
7. Oblique vein of left atrium
8. Left atrium
9. Pericardium reflection
10. Coronary sinus
11. Left ventricle
12. Apex
13. Brachiocephalic trunk
14. Arch of aorta
15. Superior vena cava
16. Right pulmonary artery
17. Right superior pulmonary vein
18. Right inferior pulmonary vein
19. Sulcus terminalis cordis
20. Right atrium
21. Inferior vena cava
22. Coronary sulcus
23. Posterior interventricular sulcus (branch of coronary artery and middle cardiac vein)
24. Right ventricle

HEART INTERSECTION

1.
2.
3.
4.
5.
6.
7.
8.
9.
10.
11.
12.
13.
14.
15.
16.
17.
18.
19.
20.

21.
22.
23.
24.
25.
26.
27.
28.
29.
30.
31.
15.
32.
19.
33.

HEART INTERSECTION

1. Posterior cusp of mitral valve
2. Anterior cusp of mitral valve
3. Right superior pulmonary vein
4. Aortic sinus (Valsalva)
5. Left semilunar cusp of aortic valve
6. Ascending aorta
7. Posterior semilunar cusp of aortic valve
8. Superior vena cava
9. Atrioventricular part of membranous septum
10. Interventricular part of membranous septum
11. Right atrium
12. Anterior cusp of tricuspid valve
13. Septal cusp of tricuspid valve
14. Posterior cusp of tricuspid valve
15. Right ventricle
16. Right anterior papillary muscle
17. Right posterior papillary muscle
18. Muscular part of intraventricular septum
19. Left ventricle
20. Left posterior papillary muscle
21. Left pulmonary veins
22. Pulmonary trunk
23. Left atrium
24. Ascending aorta
25. Opening of coronary arteries
26. Right auricle
27. Left semilunar cusp of aortic valve
28. Right semilunar cusp of aortic valve
29. Supraventricular crest
30. Outflow to pulmonary trunk
31. Right anterior papillary muscle
32. Moderator band of septomarginal trabecula
33. Left anterior papillary muscle

MUSCLES OF ANTERIOR ABDOMINAL WALL

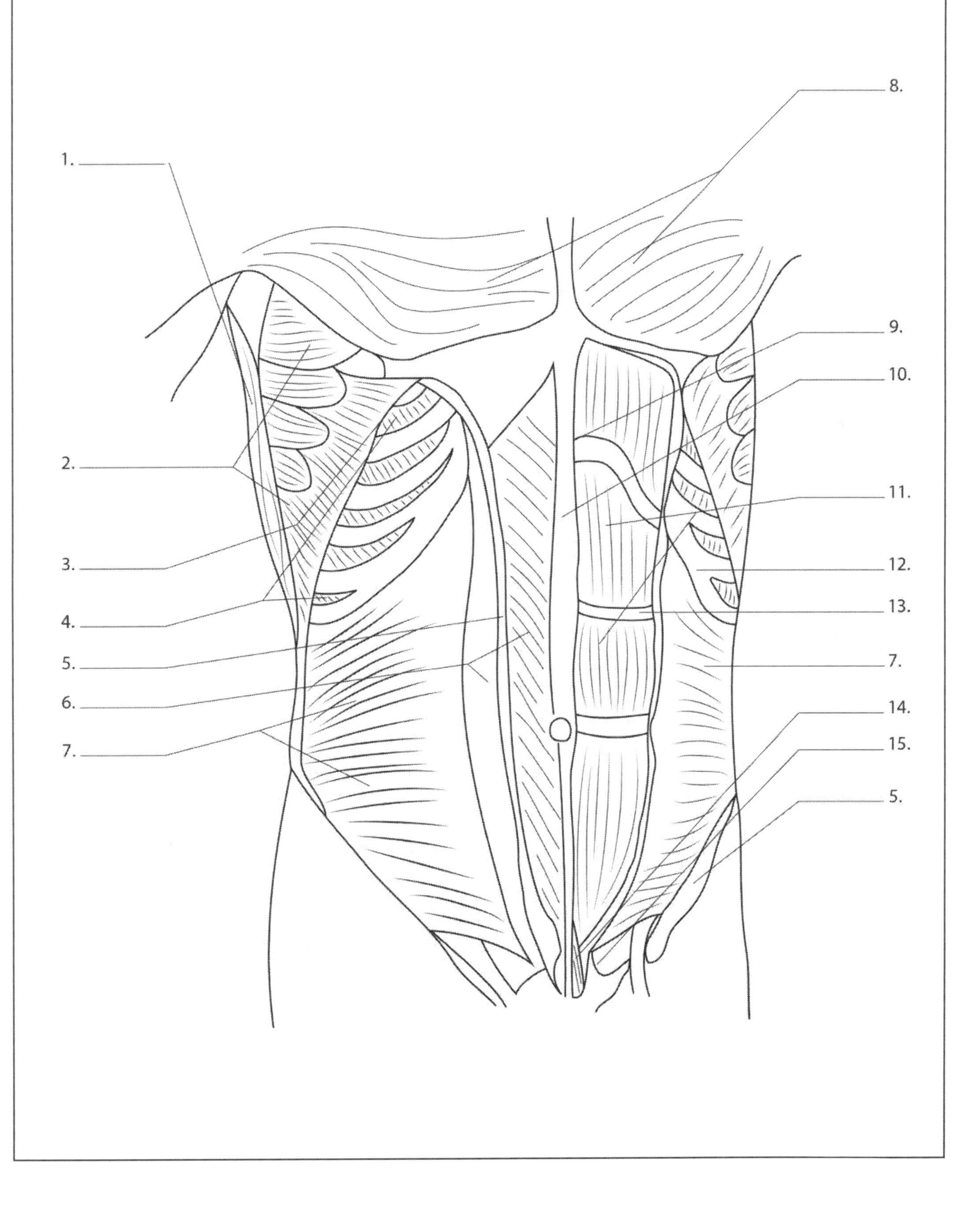

MUSCLES OF ANTERIOR ABDOMINAL WALL

1. Muscle latissimus dorsa
2. Muscle serratus anterior
3. Muscle external abdominal oblique
4. Muscle external intercostal
5. External oblique aponeurosis
6. Rectus sheath
7. Muscle internal abdominal oblique
8. Muscle pectoralis major
9. Anterior layer of rectus sheath
10. Linea alba
11. Muscle rectus abdominal
12. Ribs
13. Tendinous intersection
14. Pyramidalis muscle
15. Pectineal ligament

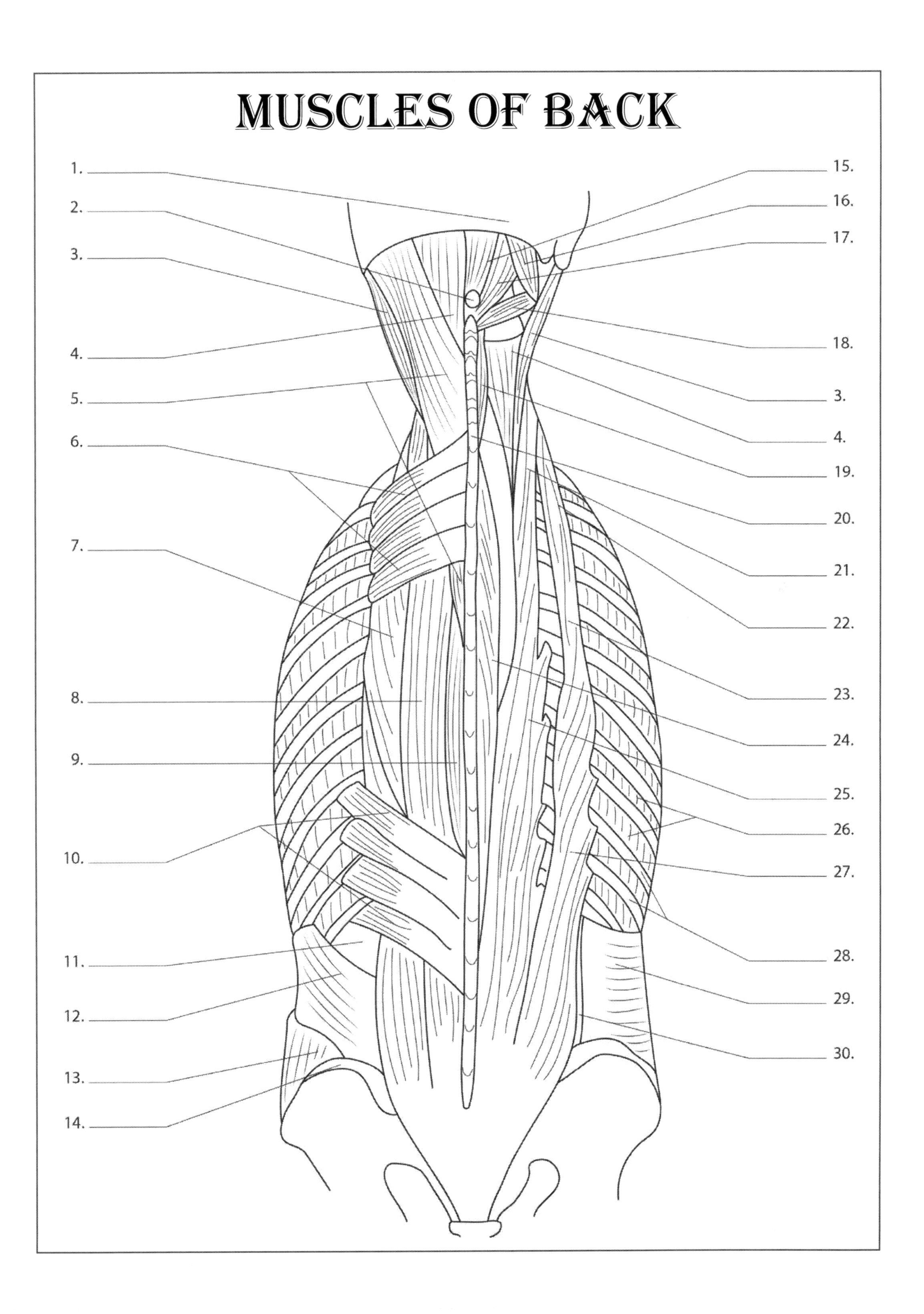
MUSCLES OF BACK
1.
2.
3.
4.
5.
6.
7.
8.
9.
10.
11.
12.
13.
14.
15.
16.
17.
18.
3.
4.
19.
20.
21.
22.
23.
24.
25.
26.
27.
28.
29.
30.

MUSCLES OF BACK

1. Superior nuchal line of scull
2. Posterior tubercle of atlas (C1)
3. Muscle longissimus capitis
4. Muscle semispinalis capitis
5. Muscle splenius capitis and splenius cervicis
6. Muscle serratus posterior superior
7. Muscle iliocostalis
8. Muscle longissimus
9. Muscle spinalis
10. Muscle serratus posterior inferior
11. Tendor of origin of transversus abdominis muscle
12. Muscle internal oblique
13. Muscle external oblique
14. Iliac crest
15. Muscle rectus capitis posterior minor
16. Muscle obliquus capitis superior
17. Muscle rectus capitis posterior major
18. Muscle oblique capitis inferior
19. Muscle spinalis cervicis
20. Spinal cord
21. Muscle longissimus cervicis
22. Muscle iliocostalis cervicis
23. Muscle iliocostalis thoracis
24. Muscle spinalis thoracis
25. Muscle longissimus thoracis
26. Muscle intercostal external
27. Muscle iliocostalis lumborum
28. Ribs
29. Muscle transversus abdominis
30. Thoracolumbar fascia

ABDOMINAL CAVITY ORGANS

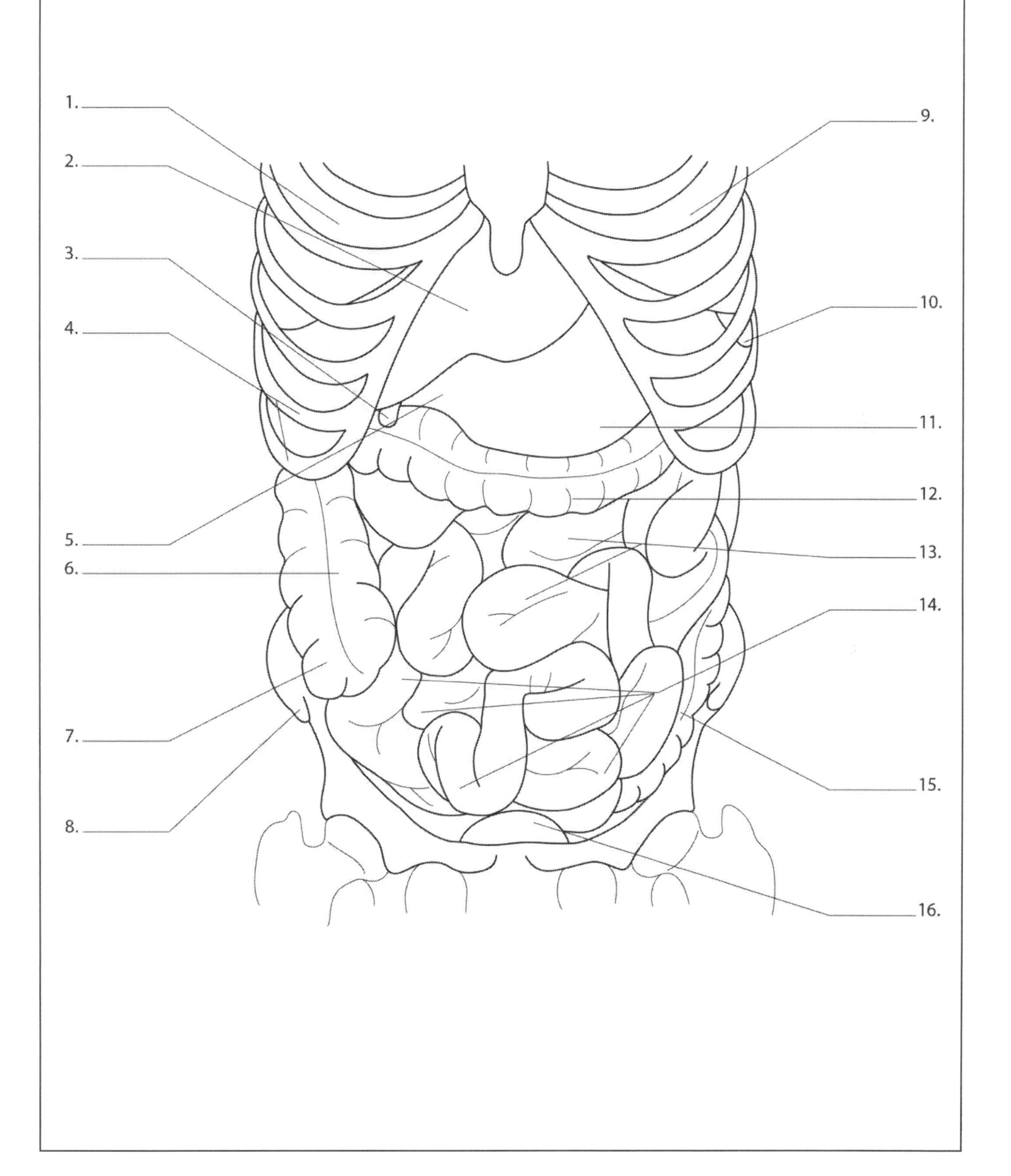

ABDOMINAL CAVITY ORGANS

1. Right lung
2. Liver
3. Fundus of gallbladder
4. Ribs
5. Pylorus
6. Ascending colon
7. Cecum
8. Anterior superior iliac spine
9. Left lung
10. Spleen
11. Body of stomach
12. Transverse colon
13. Jejunum
14. Ileum
15. Descending colon
16. Urinary bladder

RETROPERITONEAL ABDOMINAL CAVITY ORGANS

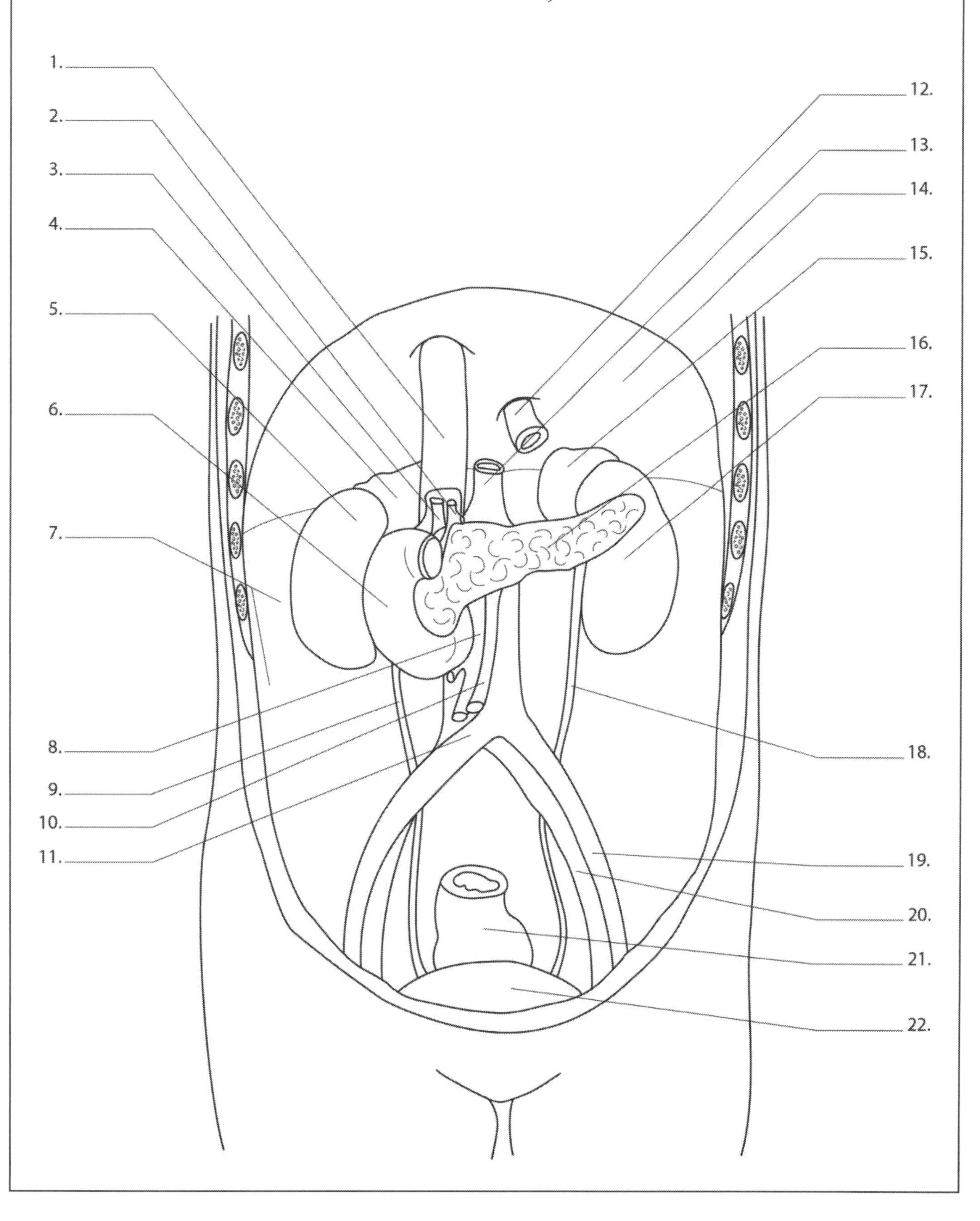

RETROPERITONEAL ABDOMINAL CAVITY ORGANS

1. Inferior vena cava
2. Hepatic artery proper
3. Common bile duct
4. Right suprarenal gland
5. Right kidney
6. Duodenum
7. Parietal peritoneum
8. Superior mesenteric vein
9. Right ureter
10. Superior mesenteric artery
11. Common iliac artery
12. Esophagus
13. Abdominal aorta
14. Diaphragm
15. Left suprarenal gland
16. Pancreas
17. Left kidney
18. Left ureter
19. External iliac artery
20. External iliac vein
21. Rectum
22. Urinary bladder

KIDNEY

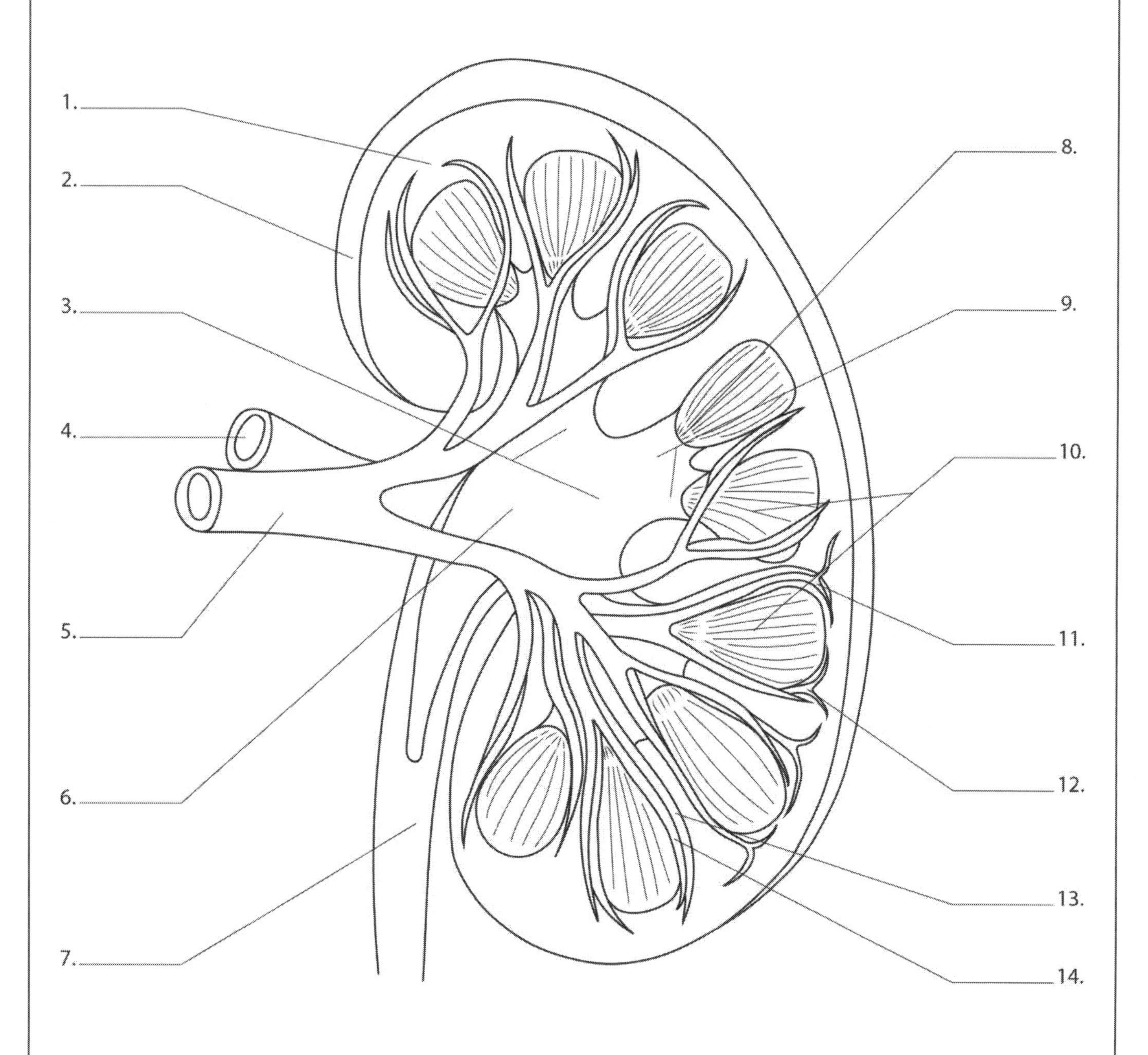

KIDNEY

1. Cortex
2. Fibrous capsule
3. Major calyxes
4. Renal artery
5. Renal vein
6. Renal pelvis
7. Ureter
8. Renal papilla
9. Minor calyxes
10. Medulla (renal pyramids)
11. Arcuate vein
12. Arcuate artery
13. Interlobular artery
14. Interlobular vein

PELVIS BONES

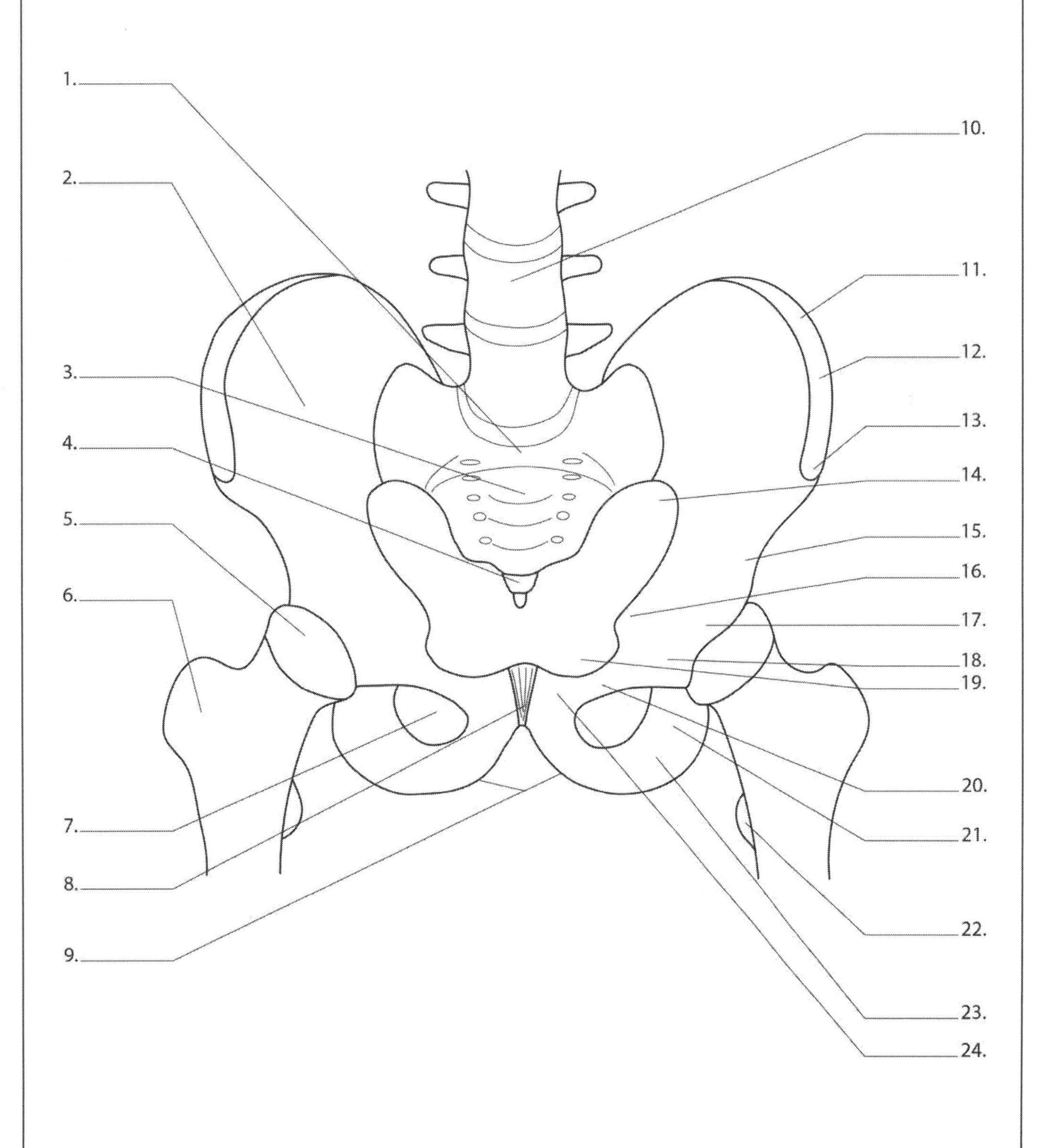

PELVIS BONES

1. Sacral promontory
2. Ala of ilium
3. Sacrum
4. Coccyx
5. Articular cartilage
6. Greater trochanter of femur
7. Obturator foramen
8. Pubic symphysis
9. Pubic arch
10. Lumbar vertebra
11. Iliac crest
12. Tubercle of iliac crest
13. Anterior superior iliac spine
14. Greater sciatic notch
15. Anterior inferior iliac spine
16. Ischial spine
17. Iliopubic eminence
18. Pectineal line
19. Lesser sciatic notch
20. Superior pubic ramus
21. Ischial tuberosity
22. Lesser trochanter of femur
23. Inferior pubic ramus
24. Pubic tubercle

FEMALE PELVIS MUSCLES

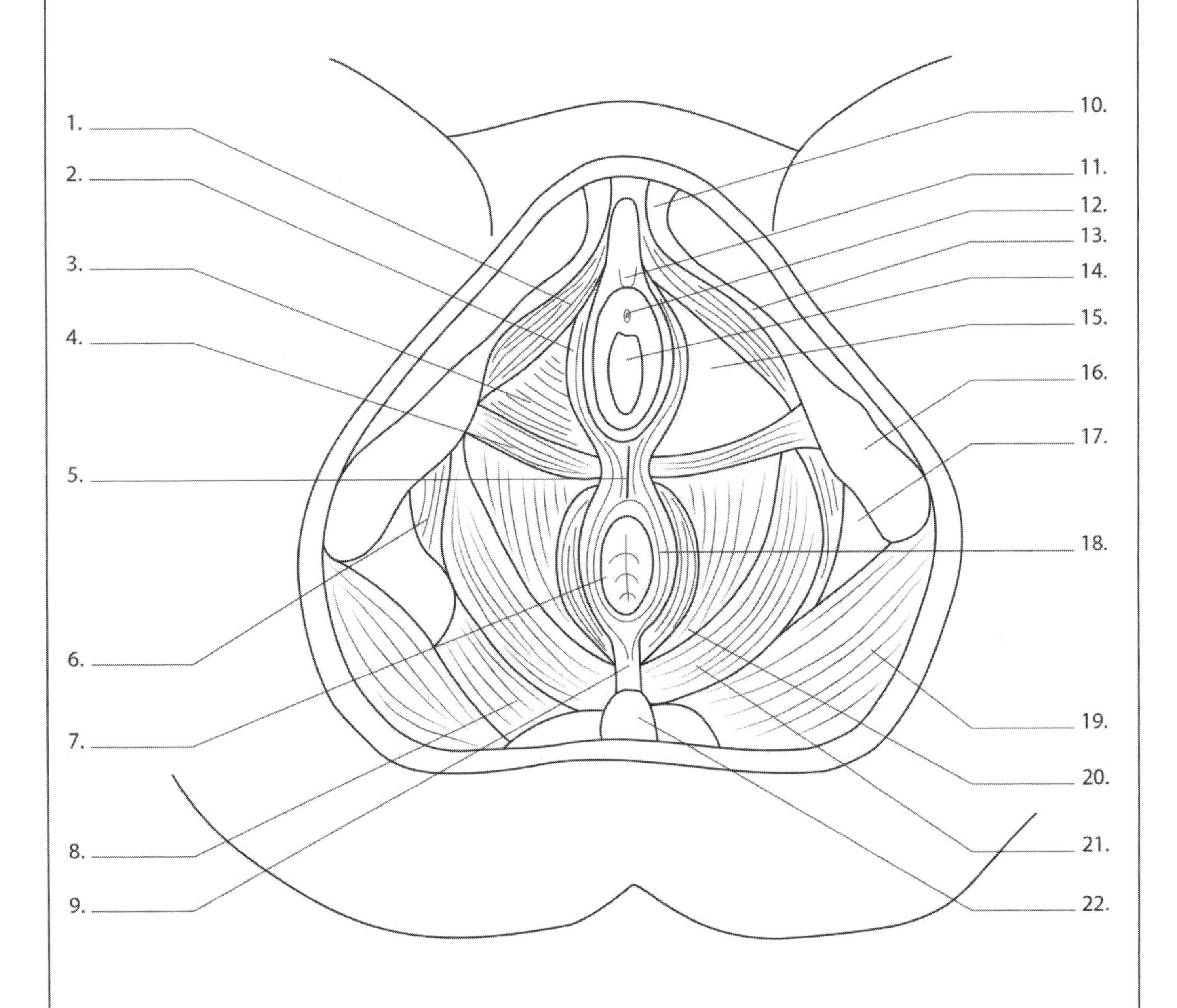

FEMALE PELVIS MUSCLES

1. Muscle ischiocavernosus
2. Muscle bulbospongiosus
3. Deep transverse perineal muscle
4. Superficial transverse perineal muscle
5. Central tendon of perineum
6. Muscle obturator internus
7. Anus
8. Muscle coccyges
9. Anococcygeal ligament
10. Inferior pubic ramus
11. Clitoris
12. Urethra
13. Ischiopubic ramus
14. Vagina
15. Perineal membrane
16. Ischial tuberosity
17. Sacro-tuberous ligament
18. External anal sphincter
19. Gluteus major
20. Muscle pubococcygeus
21. Muscle iliococcygeus
22. Coccyx

MALE PELVIS MUSCLE

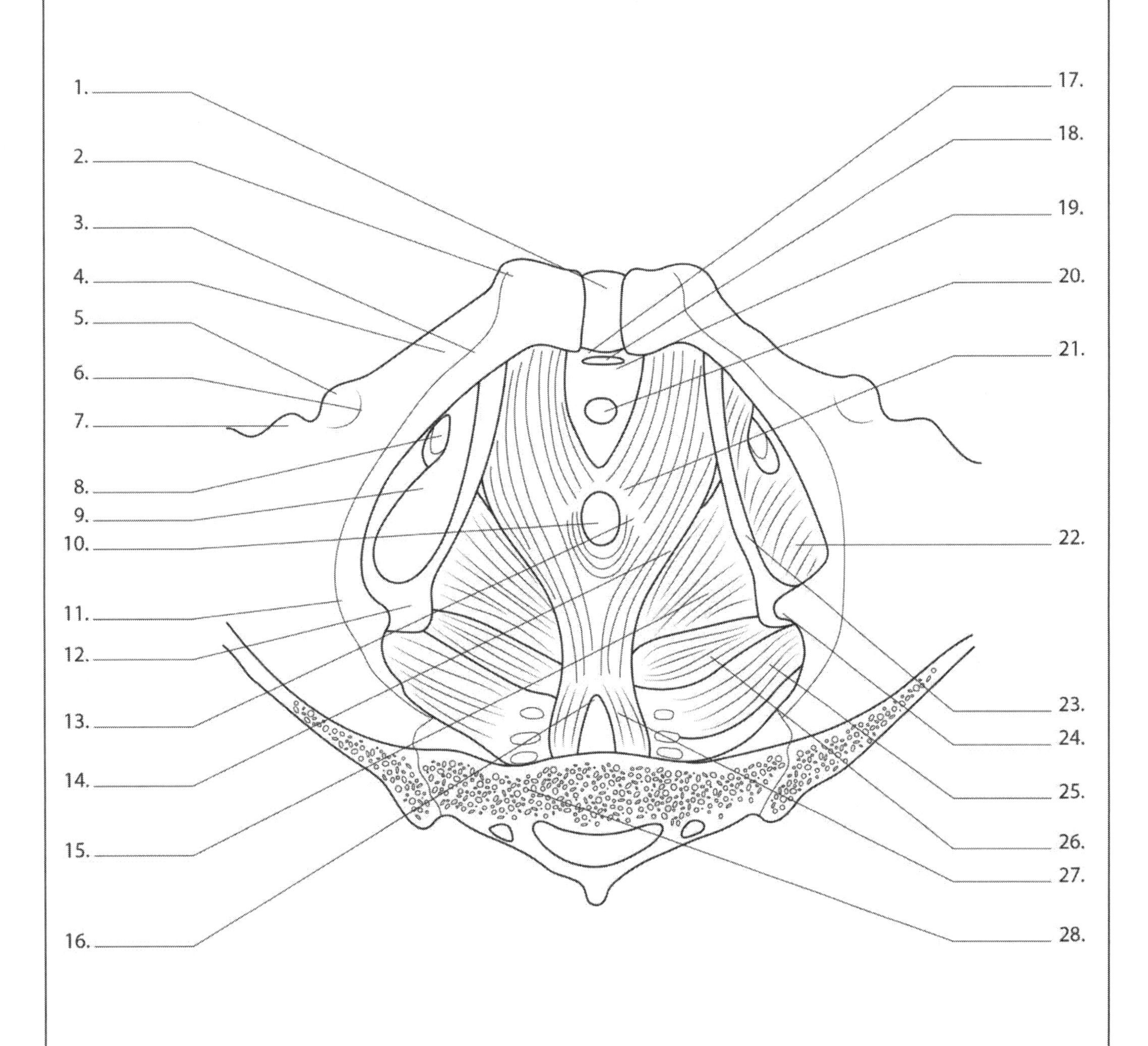

MALE PELVIS MUSCLE

1. Pubic symphysis
2. Pubic crest
3. Pecten pubis
4. Superior ramus of pubis
5. Rim of acetabulum
6. Iliopubic eminence
7. Anterior inferior iliac spine
8. Obturator canal
9. Obturator fascia
10. Anorectal hiatus
11. Arcuate line (iliac part of iliopectineal line)
12. Ischial spine
13. Puborectalis muscle
14. Pubococcygeus muscle
15. Iliococcygeus muscle
16. Coccyx
17. Inferior pubic ligament
18. Hiatus for deep dorsal vein of penis
19. Transverse perineal ligament
20. Hiatus for urethra
21. Muscle fibers from levator ani
22. Muscle obturator internus
23. Tendinous arch of levator ani muscle
24. Ischial spine
25. Piriformis muscle
26. Muscle coccygeus
27. Anterior sacrococcygeus ligament
28. Sacrum

FEMALE PELVIS MUSCLES

1. ....
2. ....
3. ....
4. ....
5. ....
6. ....
7. ....
8. ....
9. ....
10. ....
11. ....
12. ....
13. ....
14. ....
15. ....
16. ....
17. ....

FEMALE PELVIS MUSCLES

1. Spinal column
2. Sigmoid column
3. Uterus
4. Rectum
5. Recto-uterine pouch
6. Cervix
7. Vaginal vault
8. Ureter
9. Fallopian tube
10. Ovary
11. Peritoneum
12. Bladder
13. Pubic symphysis
14. Vesico-uterus pouch
15. Urethra
16. Vagina
17. Anus

MALE PELVIS ORGANS

1. ....
2. ....
3. ....
4. ....
5. ....
6. ....
7. ....
8. ....
9. ....
10. ....
11. ....
12. ....
13. ....
14. ....
15. ....
16. ....
17. ....
18. ....
19. ....
20. ....
21. ....
22. ....
23. ....
24. ....
25. ....
26. ....
27. ....
28. ....

MALE PELVIS ORGANS

1. Peritoneum
2. Prostate gland
3. Ductus deferens
4. Pubic symphysis
5. Suspensory ligament of penis
6. Corpus cavernosum
7. Corpus spongiosum
8. Corona of glans penis
9. Glans penis
10. Navicular fossa of urethra
11. External urethral opening
12. Epididymis
13. Muscle sphincter urethrae
14. Ureter
15. Sacrum
16. Urinary bladder
17. Opening of ureter
18. Ampulla of ductus deferens
19. Rectovesical pouch
20. Seminal vesicle
21. Rectum
22. Muscle levator ani
23. Anococcygeal ligament
24. Internal anal sphincter
25. External anal sphincter
26. Anus
27. Ejaculatory duct
28. Bulbourethral gland and duct

Skeleton (Front View)

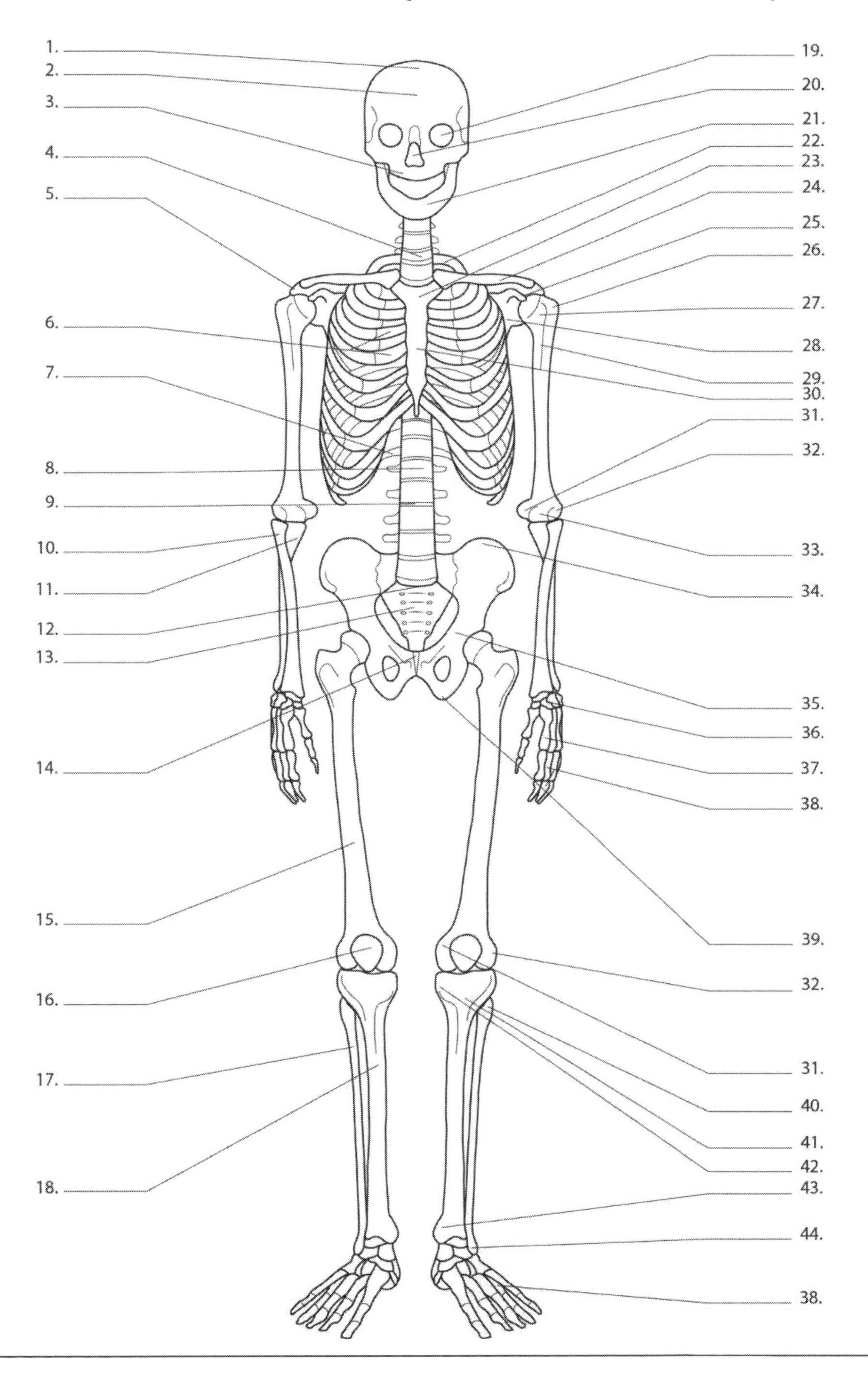

SKELETON (FRONT VIEW)

1. Skull
2. Frontal bone
3. Maxilla
4. C7 vertebra
5. Acromion
6. Costal cartilage
7. 12th rib
8. L1 vertebra
9. Intervertebral discs
10. Radius
11. Ulna
12. S1 vertebra
13. Sacrum
14. Pubic symphysis
15. Femur
16. Patella
17. Fibula
18. Tibia
19. Orbital cavity
20. Nasal cavity
21. Mandible
22. 1st rib
23. Manubrium
24. Clavicle
25. Coracoid process
26. Greater tubercle
27. Lesser tubercle
28. Scapula
29. Humerus
30. Sternum
31. Medial epicondyle
32. Lateral epicondyle
33. Capitulum of humerus
34. Ilium
35. Pubis
36. Carpals
37. Metacarpals
38. Phalanges
39. Ischium
40. Head of fibula
41. Tibia tuberosity
42. Medial tibia condyle
43. Medial malleolus
44. Lateral malleolus

SKELETON (BACK VIEW)

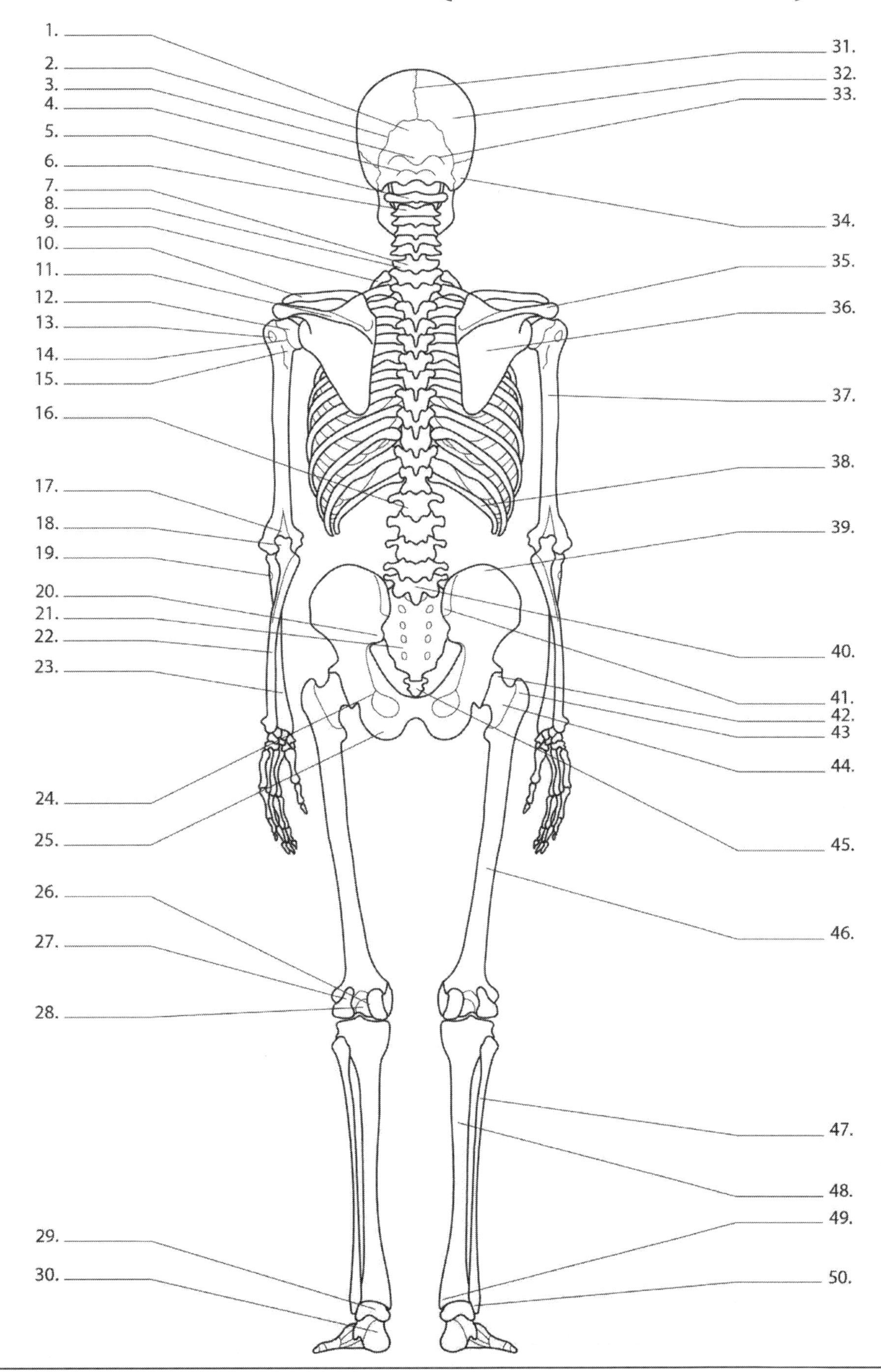

SKELETON (BACK VIEW)

1. Occipital
2. Lambdoid suture
3. External occipital protuberance
4. Inferior nuchal line
5. Atlas (C1)
6. Axis (C2)
7. C7 vertebra
8. T1 vertebra
9. 1st rib
10. Clavicle
11. Spine of scapula
12. Head of humerus
13. Greater tubercle
14. Anatomic neck
15. Surgical neck
16. L1 vertebra
17. Olecranon fossa
18. Olecranon
19. Radial tuberosity
20. Posterior inferior iliac spine
21. Sacrum
22. Ulna
23. Radius
24. Ischial spine
25. Ischial tuberosity
26. Medial femoral condyle
27. Lateral femoral condyle
28. Intercondylar fossa
29. Talus
30. Calcaneus
31. Sagittal suture
32. Parietal bone
33. Superior nuchal line
34. Temporal bone
35. Acromion
36. Scapula
37. Humerus
38. 12th rib
39. Ilium
40. L5 vertebra
41. Posterior superior iliac spine
42. Head of femur
43. Greater trochanter
44. Neck of femur
45. Coccyx
46. Femur
47. Fibula
48. Tibia
49. Medial malleolus
50. Lateral malleolus

Made in the USA
Columbia, SC
15 February 2021